Ben and Boots

by Pauline Cartwright
illustrated by Meredith Thomas

Harcourt
SCHOOL PUBLISHERS

Printed in China

ISBN 10: 0-15-350399-8
ISBN 13: 978-0-15-350399-3

Ordering Options
ISBN 10: 0-15-350332-7 (Grade 2 Below-Level Collection)
ISBN 13: 978-0-15-350332-0 (Grade 2 Below-Level Collection)
ISBN 10: 0-15-357426-7 (package of 5)
ISBN 13: 978-0-15-357426-9 (package of 5)

6 7 8 9 10   985   15 14 13 12 11 10 09

Ben and Sooty

by Pauline Cartwright
Illustrated by Meredith Thomas

Harcourt

Ben joined the children watching
the kittens in the pet store.

Ben wanted a kitten. Which kitten would Ben like most?

4

Finally, Ben chose a kitten with short, black fur.
He called his kitten Sooty.

Ben gave Sooty food.
He played games with her.

Each night, Sooty slept in her
basket. She slept near Ben.

One morning, Sooty wasn't there.
Ben called Sooty, but she didn't
come.

Mom helped Ben look for Sooty.

Dad helped Ben look, too.
"Sooty is always in her basket!"
said Ben.

"She *is* in the basket," Mom said.
"She's in *this* basket."

Sooty was sleeping on top of
some sweaters.
"Sooty!" cried Ben.
"There you are!"

Ben rubbed Sooty's ears.
"Why didn't you come?"
Ben asked.
"I called you a hundred times."

That night, Ben put an old
sweater in Sooty's basket.
The next morning, Sooty
was there.
She was asleep and very cozy.

Think Critically

1. Where do you think Ben got Sooty?

2. How do you think Ben felt when he couldn't find Sooty?

3. How did the family find Sooty?

4. Why do you think Ben called his kitten Sooty?

5. Would you like a kitten? Why or why not?

 Social Studies

Write a Paragraph Ben got Sooty from a pet store. Write a paragraph to tell about why customers (buyers) might want to buy a pet and why the pet store owner (the seller) might be selling pets.

 School-Home Connection Talk about *Ben and Sooty* with a family member. Talk about the things you need to do to care for a pet.

Word Count: 152